MARVEL
COMICS
™

CONTENTS

Pedigree®
BOOKS
Published by Pedigree Books Limited
The Old Rectory, Matford Lane, Exeter, EX2 4PS

MARVEL® COMICS

£6.99
ML3

WELCOME TO THE MARVEL UNIVERSE!

As we enter a new millennium, so the super heroes and super villains of The World's Greatest Comics enter their seventh decade of adventures in the Marvel Universe.

Where is the Marvel Universe?

The Marvel Universe has no special boundaries. Its super heroes and super villains operate all over the galaxy, from Marvel's base in New York City to real and fictional corners of the earth and beyond into space and distant alien empires.

When is the Marvel Universe?

The Marvel Universe is unrestricted in time as well as space. Over the past sixty years, Marvel stories have been set as far back as medieval times and ranged through the present to way into the future with the Marvel 2099 series.

Of the numerous super heroes created over the years, featured in this annual are main players The Incredible Hulk, The Fantastic Four and the X-Men. First, though, we kick off with a crossover starring Spider-Man and the Silver Surfer, so sit back and enjoy. And if any of your favourites are missing, there's always next year's annual!

6

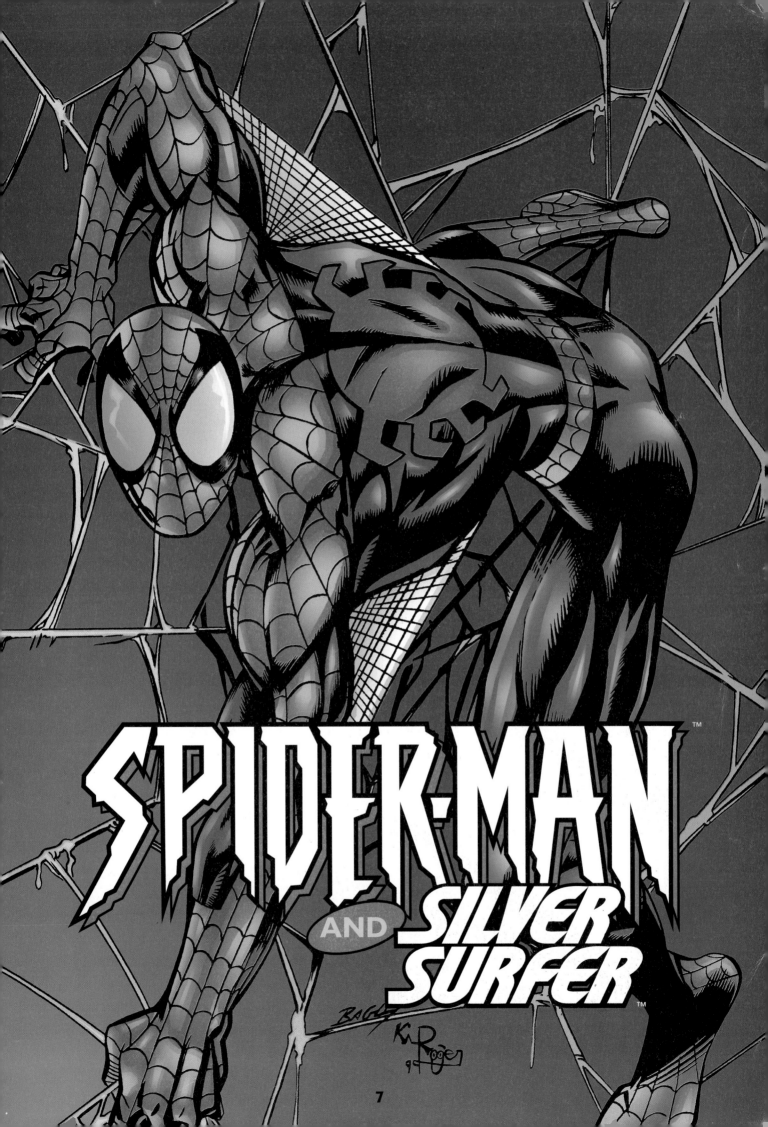

Profile: *THE AMAZING SPIDER-MAN*

Peter Parker was a hard-working high school student until the day he was bitten by an irradiated spider at a science exhibition. He suddenly found he possessed the relative climbing ability, speed, agility and strength of a spider, as well as a premonitional 'spider sense'. He began to use these powers to fight New York City's criminal element after the murder of his guardian, his beloved Uncle Ben.

Real name: Peter Parker

Super hero qualities: Possesses superhuman strength and gravity-defying climbing ability; has an early-warning danger sense.

Weapon: Wrist devices (web shooters) that shoot out tough, highly-adhesive webs.

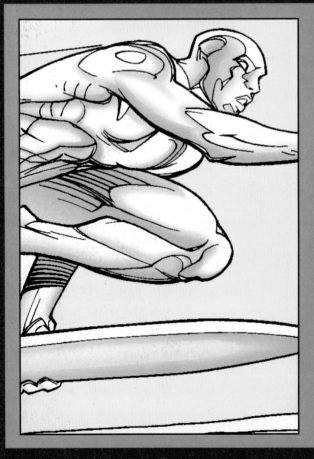

Profile: *THE SILVER SURFER*

In need of a herald to seek out suitable nourishment for him, the planet-devouring Galactus transformed Norrin Radd into a silver being that could travel through the spaceways of the universe. Having sacrificed himself in exchange for Galactus sparing his planet, Zenn-La, the Silver Surfer did his duty until Galactus tried to devour Earth. He then rebelled and used his powers to protect the innocent.

Real name: Norrin Radd

Super hero qualities: Shoots through space on 'surfboard' beyond the speed of light; can withstand rigours of constant space travel.

Weapon: Shoots highly destructive beams from his hands.

STREAKING ACROSS THE TRACKLESS VOID OF SPACE, A COSMIC-POWERED WANDERER MOVES WITH AN URGENCY UNUSUAL EVEN BY HIS FASTER-THAN-LIGHT STANDARD.

HIS NAME IS THE SILVER SURFER, AND ON THIS DAY THOUGHTS OF IMPENDING DANGER DRIVE HIM TOWARD HIS DESTINATION--

--A SMALL BLUE BALL THAT SPINS INNOCENTLY AROUND A YELLOW SUN.

IT IS A PLANET HE HAS VISITED BEFORE. ITS INHABITANTS CALL IT EARTH.

Stan Lee Presents:

FIRST CONTACT

BOB BUDIANSKY
WRITER
ALEX SAVIUK
PENCILER
AL MILGROM
INKER
J. UM BABGINS
LETTERER
KEVIN TINSLEY
COLORIST
MARK BERNARDO
EDITOR
BOB HARRAS
EDITOR IN CHIEF

MEANWHILE, FAR BELOW, AT NEW YORK CITY'S *AMERICAN MUSEUM OF NATURAL SCIENCES*...

...DR. TAYLOR COPPERTHWAITE, THE MUSEUM'S DIRECTOR, HOLDS A PRESS CONFERENCE...

LADIES AND GENTLEMEN, YOU ARE ABOUT TO WITNESS WHAT MAY BE ONE OF THE *MOST IMPORTANT* NEWS STORIES OF THE CENTURY...

...PERHAPS OF *ALL TIME!*

LIKE MOST JOURNALISTS, HOWEVER, PETER PARKER IS A SKEPTIC BY NATURE...

YEAH, YEAH. ENOUGH TALK!

IF J. JONAH JAMESON WANTED A PICTURE OF A BLOWHARD FOR THE DAILY BUGLE...

...HIS OWN UGLY MUG WOULD BE ON THE FRONT PAGE EVERY DAY!

BENEATH THIS SHROUD IS AN OBJECT THAT MAY HARBOR WITHIN IT SECRETS OF THE UNIVERSE... PERHAPS EVEN *LIFE ITSELF!*

I PRESENT TO YOU...

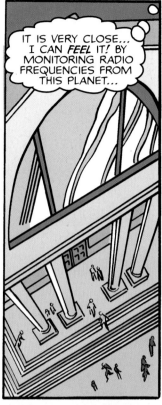

AND WHAT "KIND" IS THAT? AS FAR AS I KNOW, *THIS* SPIDER-MAN IS *ONE* OF A KIND!

DO NOT *INTERFERE!* FOR YOUR OWN SAFETY, YOU MUST GIVE ME THE METEOR!

I WOULDN'T EVEN GIVE YOU THE TIME OF DAY!

NOW, UNLESS YOU CAN FLASH SOME PRESS CREDENTIALS...

...I'LL HAVE TO ASK YOU TO *LEAVE!*

SKRAKK

Umm... PRETTY IMPRESSIVE CREDENTIALS!

WHAT HAVE I GOTTEN MYSELF INTO?! I'LL BET THIS GUY CAN LEVEL THIS WHOLE BLOCK WITH A SNAP OF HIS FINGERS!

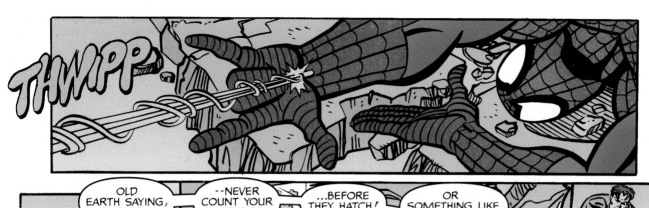

OLD EARTH SAYING, SURFER--

--NEVER COUNT YOUR *METEORS*...

...BEFORE THEY HATCH!

OR SOMETHING LIKE THAT!

NO!!!

HERE'S THE OPPORTUNITY I'VE BEEN WAITING FOR!

WITH SPIDER-MAN STILL BURIED UNDER THE DEBRIS...

...AND THE HUMANOID RECOVERING FROM HIS FALL...

...THE METEOR IS *MINE!*

OKAY, LET'S WRAP THIS UP ALREADY! I'VE GOT LAUNDRY TO DO TONIGHT!

--ALL THIS-- THE DAMAGE, THE THEFT-- COULD HAVE BEEN AVOIDED IF YOU HAD ONLY LISTENED TO ME...

...AND *NOT* INTERFERED.

THE REASON FOR OUR CONFLICT HAS DISAPPEARED, SPIDER-MAN. WHILE WE FOUGHT, SOMEONE ELSE STOLE THE METEOR AND ESCAPED.

SO I LEAVE YOU NEITHER DEFEATED NOR VICTORIOUS... ONLY WITH THESE WORDS TO PONDER--

SNAPPED MY WEBBING RIGHT IN TWO... UNDERESTIMATED HIS POWER...

GOTTA... STOP HIM..

I'VE WASTED TOO MUCH TIME FIGHTING YOU TO STAY HERE A MOMENT LONGER, SPIDER-MAN. I CAN'T RISK ANOTHER BOUT WITH THE AUTHORITIES.

...FOLLOW HIM...

...TOO WEAK... SPIDER-TRACER IS THE ONLY CHANCE...

...TO TRACK HIM...

...AND I WILL DESTROY YOU!

BUT BE WARNED-- SHOULD WE MEET AGAIN, I'LL BE READY FOR YOU...!

BUT THE LOOTER'S THREAT GOES UNHEARD..

A VALIANT EFFORT, HUMAN... BUT FOR NAUGHT! YOUR STRENGTH PALES BEFORE THAT OF THE LOOTER-- A MAN WHOSE VEINS PULSE WITH STAR-SPAWNED POWER!

I AM CERTAIN YOU REALIZE THIS...

WOMP

...AS SPIDER-MAN FINALLY LOSES CONSCIOUSNESS.

...AS CERTAIN AS I AM THAT, LIKE SO MANY OF YOUR RACE, YOU ARE FAR TOO STUBBORN TO BE DETERRED BY OVERWHELMING ODDS. AND THAT IS A FLAW I PLAN TO USE...

...TO MY ADVANTAGE.

22

TERRIFIC, PARKER! JUST *TERRIFIC!*

AND WHAT MAKES THESE PICTURES EVEN *BETTER* IS THEY'RE *PROOF* OF HOW *OVERRATED* SPIDER-MAN REALLY IS!

JUST *LOOK* AT THE LOOTER MOPPING THE FLOOR WITH THAT COSTUMED CREEP!

YES... I *THOUGHT* YOU'D LIKE THAT, MR. JAMESON.

AND I BET YOU'D BE EVEN *HAPPIER* IF THEY SHOWED THE LOOTER WITH MY HEAD ON A STICK!

I DON'T KNOW HOW YOU DO IT, PARKER. SOMETIMES YOUR PHOTOS ARE SO GOOD THEY'RE *ALMOST* WORTH THE INFLATED SUMS I PAY YOU FOR THEM!

WHY, THANK YOU, MR. JAMESON...

...YOU UNGRATEFUL CHEAPSKATE!

WITH WHAT YOU PAY ME, I CAN BARELY AFFORD TO TAKE THE *SUBWAY.*

BUT THAT'S THE LEAST OF MY PROBLEMS. I HAVEN'T PICKED UP A SIGNAL FROM THE TRACER I PLANTED ON THE LOOTER YET. MAYBE IT'S MALFUNCTIONING!

MISS GRANT, WHY DON'T YOU SHOW PARKER THE *DAILY BUGLE'S* APPRECIATION BY TAKING HIM TO LUNCH.. ON ME, OF COURSE.

WHY, THAT'S VERY KIND OF YOU, MR. JAMESON!

TWO DOLLARS?!

C'MON, PETER. I'LL SPLIT A *CANDY BAR* WITH YOU.

SURE. THAT'S THE BEST OFFER I'VE HAD ALL DAY-- *Hmmm?*

SPIDER-SENSE TINGLING ALL OF A SUDDEN! THE TRACER'S WORKING AGAIN!

Umm... ON SECOND THOUGHT, I'LL HAVE TO TAKE A RAIN CHECK ON THAT CANDY BAR, GLORY!

I JUST REMEMBERED -- I'M ON A *SUGAR-FREE DIET!*

23

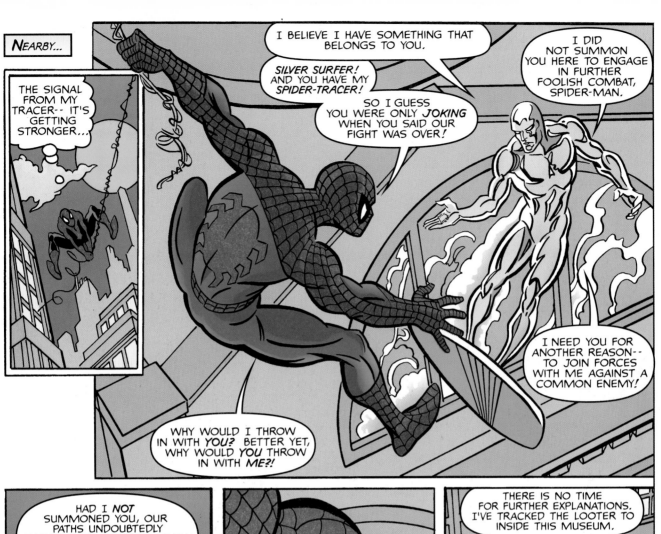

THE SIGNAL FROM MY TRACER-- IT'S GETTING STRONGER...

I BELIEVE I HAVE SOMETHING THAT BELONGS TO YOU.

SILVER SURFER! AND YOU HAVE MY SPIDER-TRACER!

SO I GUESS YOU WERE ONLY JOKING WHEN YOU SAID OUR FIGHT WAS OVER!

I DID NOT SUMMON YOU HERE TO ENGAGE IN FURTHER FOOLISH COMBAT, SPIDER-MAN.

I NEED YOU FOR ANOTHER REASON-- TO JOIN FORCES WITH ME AGAINST A COMMON ENEMY!

WHY WOULD I THROW IN WITH YOU? BETTER YET, WHY WOULD YOU THROW IN WITH ME?!

HAD I NOT SUMMONED YOU, OUR PATHS UNDOUBTEDLY WOULD HAVE CROSSED AGAIN, WHICH MIGHT HAVE LED TO ANOTHER ILL-ADVISED CONFRONTATION.

RATHER THAN TAKE THE RISK, I THOUGHT IT PREFERABLE WE WORK TOGETHER.

I FOUND YOUR TRACER AT THE JEWELRY ESTABLISHMENT AND JAMMED ITS SIGNAL WITH AN ELECTROMAGNETIC FIELD UNTIL A FEW HOURS AGO WHEN I FINALLY REQUIRED YOUR PRESENCE.

WAITASEC, CHROME-DOME! YOU MEAN TO SAY YOU WERE THERE WHILE THE LOOTER WAS POUNDING ME INTO THE GROUND... AND YOU DID NOTHING TO STOP HIM?!

THAT WOULD HAVE DEFEATED THE WHOLE PURPOSE OF MY BEING THERE!

AND WHAT WAS THAT-- TO GET YOUR LAUGHS WATCHING ME GET MY BUTT KICKED?!

THERE IS NO TIME FOR FURTHER EXPLANATIONS. I'VE TRACKED THE LOOTER TO INSIDE THIS MUSEUM.

COME!

SURE, WHY NOT? I HAVEN'T DONE ANYTHING REALLY STUPID FOR AT LEAST 24 HOURS!

I'M DUE!

27

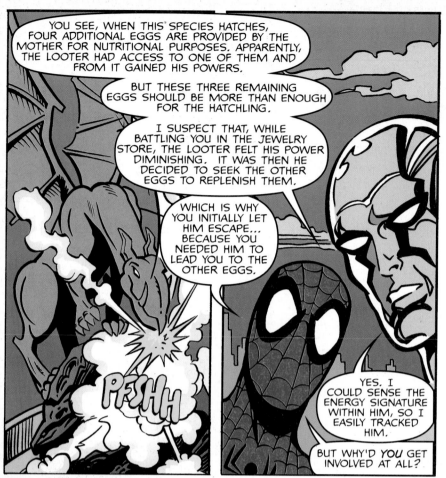

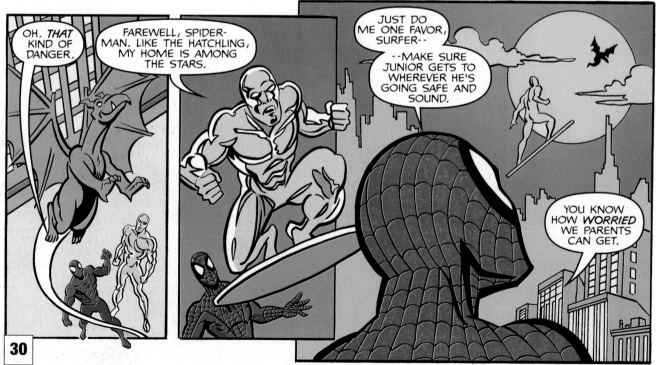

THE END.

WORD TRAIL

Hidden in the Silver Surfer's trail, reading forwards or backwards, you can find the names of four of his nemeses. The answers are at the bottom of the page.

B
E
S O
N A H T U S
L A O S M
S A O T S I H P E M
U T C A
T C O A
O C O D L P G
R T D O M
O R D O O M T
W

BREAKING THROUGH

The Incredible Hulk is on the rampage again and nothing can stop him. How many bricks has he just punched out of the wall? The answer is at the bottom of the page.

Answer: There are 46 bricks missing from the wall.

32

THE INCREDIBLE HULK

Profile: THE INCREDIBLE HULK

Mild-mannered research scientist Bruce Banner was the inventor of the 'G-Bomb', an atomic weapon that released lethal gamma radiation. Whilst trying to save a teenager who had strayed on to the test sight, Banner was irradiated with what should have been a lethal dose of gamma rays, but did not die. He would instead undergo a dramatic transformation whenever he was angry to become a seven foot, green-skinned monster with the strength of two hundred men.

Real name: Bruce Banner

Occupation: Nuclear physicist

Base of operations: New Mexico

Super hero qualities: Possesses high degree of resistance to injury, pain and disease. His superhuman strength enables him to lift in excess of 100 tons.

Weapon: None

Height: 7 ft.

Weight: 1040 lbs.

Stan Lee PRESENTS:

THE MONSTER AND THE IMMORTAL

THE NEW MEXICAN DESERT, WHERE SCIENTIST ROBERT BRUCE BANNER AWAITS THE ARRIVAL OF FRIENDS...

HERE THEY COME--RICK JONES AND BETTY ROSS... PERHAPS THE ONLY TWO PEOPLE IN THIS WORLD I CAN TRUST.

RALPH MACCHIO - WRITER
ANDY KUHN - PENCILER
HARRY CANDELARIO - INKER
MICHUL HIGGINS - LETTERER
KEVIN TINSLEY - COLORIST
MARK BERNARDO - EDITOR
BOB HARRAS - ED. IN CHIEF

HEY-- *GREAT* TO SEE YOU BOTH!

THE RIDE WAS A LITTLE BUMPY--AND WE HAD TO AVOID A FEW DOZEN GILA MONSTERS--

--BUT IT WAS *WORTH* IT.

DOC, HOW'S IT GOIN'?

MAKES ME FEEL GOOD SEEING THEM GET A CHANCE TO BE *TOGETHER* FOR A CHANGE.

WITH ALL THAT'S HAPPENED OVER THE PAST FEW MONTHS--ALL THE TURMOIL AND TRAGEDY...

...AND IT'S MY *FAULT.* ALL OF IT.

"THERE I WAS, PARKING MY WHEELS...JUST WANTING TO SOAK UP SOME DESERT SUN--

"--LITTLE REALIZING THAT I'D PULLED OVER AT THE TEST SITE OF SOMETHING CALLED THE *GAMMA BOMB.*

"DOCTOR BANNER--THE BOMB'S CREATOR--SAW ME AND RUSHED OUT TO GET ME TO SAFETY.

"BECAUSE THE BOMB WAS ONLY SECONDS FROM DETONATION, BRUCE JUST HAD TIME TO THROW ME INTO A NEARBY DITCH.

"UNFORTUNATELY, THE DOC HIMSELF DIDN'T MAKE IT AND WAS CAUGHT IN THE BOMB'S BLAST.

"THE GAMMA RADIATION WENT THROUGH *EVERY* PORE OF HIS BODY.

"BUT HE *WASN'T* KILLED--SOMETHING MUCH *WORSE* HAPPENED TO THE POOR GUY.

36

"WHEN HE GETS STRESSED OR ANGRY, BRUCE NOW TRANSFORMS INTO A MONSTROUS CREATURE THE MILITARY'S NAMED-- *THE HULK!*

"BECAUSE OF THAT, BRUCE HAD TO FLEE GAMMA BASE AND HIDE OUT HERE IN THE DESERT. SO BETTY'S FATHER, GENERAL ROSS, HAS GOT THE ARMY HOT ON BRUCE'S TRAIL.

"I'VE TRIED TO HELP BRUCE -- KEEPING HIM LOCKED BEHIND A TWENTY-TON ROCK DOOR WHEN THE TRANSFORMATION'S ON HIM.

"IT'S THE *LEAST* I CAN DO BECAUSE *I'M* THE CAUSE OF THIS HORROR.

"THAT MAN RISKED HIS *LIFE* TO SAVE *MINE*... AND I'LL *NEVER* ABANDON HIM, NEVER."

I WISH I HAD SOME GOOD NEWS, BUT OL' THUNDERBOLT ROSS IS SPENDING EVERY WAKING MINUTE TRYING TO TRACK YOU DOWN.

IT MAY NOT BE SAFE FOR YOU OUT HERE IN THE DESERT ANY LONGER.

BUT, RICK, IF I HID OUT IN A *POPULATED* AREA, IMAGINE WHAT WOULD HAPPEN IF I BECAME THE HULK!

THAT'S MY BRUCE... ALWAYS THINKING OF OTHERS' WELFARE -- NEVER HIS OWN.

Y'KNOW, THAT'S WHY I LOVE YOU, DR. BANNER.

C'MON, BETTY.

LISTEN, I MAY BE ON THE VERGE OF DEVELOPING A MACHINE THAT COULD *CONTROL* MY TRANSFORMATIONS.

I'VE GOT ALL MY EQUIPMENT IN THE CAVE SO EVEN AN EARTHQUAKE COULDN'T GET ME TO LEAVE.

FOR HOURS THEY DESCEND INTO THE DEPTHS OF THE PLANET... THROUGH DARK, DANK TUNNELS THAT SEEM TO HONEYCOMB ENDLESSLY...

THEN, THE UNCONSCIOUS SCIENTIST REGAINS HIS FACULTIES...

...AND THE SIGHT WHICH GREETS HIS JUST-OPENING EYES IS ALMOST INCOMPREHENSIBLE.

MY GOD! WHERE AM I?

"IT LOOKS LIKE SOME ANCIENT ROMAN CITY-- PERFECTLY PRESERVED!"

I'M BEING BROUGHT INTO SOME MASSIVE DINING HALL.

I GUESS THERE'S NO REASON I SHOULD FEIGN UNCONSCIOUSNESS ANY LONGER.

MOMENTS LATER, AFTER BEING SEATED AT THE HEAD OF A HUGE TABLE...

THAT FIGURE WHICH JUST ENTERED... THE WAY THEY'RE FAWNING OVER HIM, HE MUST BE THE MASTER HERE.

GREETINGS, DR. BANNER. YES -- I KNOW WHO YOU ARE -- AMONG THE WORLD'S FOREMOST SCIENTISTS -- CREATOR OF THE DREADED GAMMA BOMB.

LET ME WELCOME YOU TO MY PORTION OF SUBTERRANEA. MY NAME IS--

-- TYRANNUS. I AM AT WAR WITH ANOTHER UNDERGROUND DWELLER -- THE MOLE MAN -- FOR CONTROL OF ALL OF SUBTERRANEA.

AND THAT IS WHY I NEED YOUR SCIENTIFIC EXPERTISE -- TO ALLOW ME TO EMERGE THE VICTOR IN THIS TITANIC STRUGGLE.

I DON'T INTEND TO--

BEFORE YOU GIVE ME YOUR ANSWER I NEED TO SHOW YOU SOMETHING. COME.

WAIT A MINUTE! LET GO OF ME!

I WILL BE TAKING YOU OUT OF THE CITY--

--TO A SMALL CAVERN WITHIN WHICH RESIDES NOTHING LESS THAN THE MOST *PRICELESS GIFT* MANKIND HAS EVER SOUGHT.

AND IT IS *HERE*-- WITHIN THIS PLACID POOL THAT I DISCOVERED QUITE BY ACCIDENT ONE DAY LONG AGO.

HOW CLEAR ITS SURFACE... HOW QUENCHING ITS WATER IS TO AN OLD MAN'S THIRST.

ALLOW ME THIS LIBATION BEFORE I CONTINUE SPEAKING.

HRRMMFF!

WHAT'VE YOU DONE -- *POISONED* YOURSELF?!

HARDLY, MY GOOD DOCTOR BANNER. I HAVE SIMPLY *REJUVENATED* MYSELF!

YOU SEE, THIS IS THE UNDERGROUND SPRING KNOWN IN MYTH AND FANCY AS--

--THE FOUNTAIN OF YOUTH!

IT WAS *UNDISCOVERED* BY THOSE ABOVE BECAUSE IT EXISTS *BELOW GROUND*-- HERE!

41

IT HAS KEPT ME YOUNG AND VIGOROUS SINCE I WAS *EXILED* HERE BY THE SORCERER *MERLIN* AGES AGO.

BUT MERLIN IS DUST AND *I* SURVIVE.

AND THE WILL TO *CONQUER* IS AS STRONG IN ME AS EVER. THAT IS WHERE *YOU* COME IN, DR. BANNER.

BUT BEFORE WE CONTINUE, LET ME PLACE A FEW DROPS OF THE SACRED LIQUID ON YOUR LIPS.

THE SENSATIONS WILL BE LIKE *NOTHING* YOU HAVE KNOWN.

I--I FEEL *STRENGTH* --AS IF EVERY CELL IN MY BODY WAS BEING *REVITALIZED!*

AS INDEED THEY ARE. BUT I HAVE ONLY GIVEN YOU A *TASTE* OF IMMORTALITY.

IF YOU WISH TO PARTAKE OF THESE WATERS FOREVER, THEN YOU MUST HELP ME TO *DEFEAT* THE MOLE MAN -- TO CONQUER *ALL* OF SUBTERRANEA!

CREATE THE WEAPONS I NEED FOR THIS CAMPAIGN AND YOU MAY IMMERSE YOURSELF IN THESE LIFE-ENHANCING WATERS *ETERNALLY!*

NEVER! NO MATTER *WHAT* YOU OFFER, I WON'T BE *CONNED* INTO CREATING WEAPONS FOR YOU TO USE AGAINST *ANYONE!*

I'D RATHER GROW *OLD* AND *DIE* LIKE EVERYONE ELSE!

ABOVE GROUND, ALONG A LONELY DESERT ROAD...

IT'S A GOOD THING WE WENT BACK TO HULKBUSTER BASE AFTER WE RECOVERED, TO GET THIS EQUIPMENT WE'LL NEED TO SEARCH FOR BRUCE.

YOUR FATHER, GENERAL ROSS, GAVE US SOME STRANGE LOOKS WHEN WE ASKED FOR THIS STUFF, THOUGH, BETTY.

HE'S JUST WORRIED ABOUT HIS LITTLE GIRL EXPLORING CAVES.

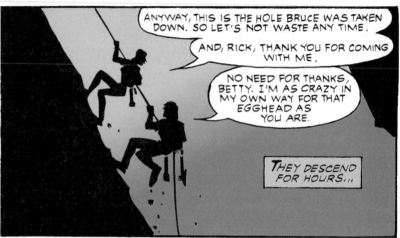

ANYWAY, THIS IS THE HOLE BRUCE WAS TAKEN DOWN. SO LET'S NOT WASTE ANY TIME.

AND, RICK, THANK YOU FOR COMING WITH ME.

NO NEED FOR THANKS, BETTY. I'M AS CRAZY IN MY OWN WAY FOR THAT EGGHEAD AS YOU ARE.

THEY DESCEND FOR HOURS...

THESE INFRARED GOGGLES ARE WONDERFUL FOR SEEING IN THE DARK.

RICK--THIS WAY... THAT ENORMOUS CAVERN THERE.

I CAN'T BELIEVE WE'VE GOTTEN SO DEEP WITHOUT BEING SPOTTED BY ONE OF THOSE CREATURES.

TZZT

Ooh-- SPOKE TOO SOON!

THERE'RE TOO MANY OF THEM, BETTY! DON'T RESIST!

SOON...

Ahh, THE YOUNG RICK JONES AND THE LOVELY MS. BETTY ROSS. I IMAGINED YOU'D ATTEMPT TO RESCUE BANNER--THUS MY PRECAUTIONS.

I HAVE BROUGHT HIM TO GREET YOU. RELEASE THEM, MY LOYAL TYRANNOIDS.

OH, BRUCE--I THOUGHT I'D *NEVER* SEE YOU AGAIN! WHO *IS* THIS AWFUL MAN? WHAT'S THIS AWFUL PLACE?

EASY, BETTY. HIS NAME IS TYRANNUS. HE RULES THIS UNDERGROUND CITY. NOW WE'RE ALL HIS PRISONERS.

EXACTLY. AND IF YOU DO NOT WANT THESE FRIENDS OF YOURS *KILLED*, YOU'LL DO PRECISELY AS I SAY, DOCTOR.

I HAVE NO DESIRE TO HARM EITHER OF THEM, BUT I HAVE DESIGNS OF *CONQUEST* ON THE REST OF SUBTERRANEA...

...AND THE SURFACE WORLD.

I MAY HAVE TO COOPERATE WITH THIS MONSTER--IF ONLY TO BUY TIME FOR BETTY AND RICK.

THINK IT OVER... BRIEFLY.

47

GET AWAY FROM HULK, UGLY MEN! *GET AWAY!*

HULK WILL HELP BOY. BOY IS HULK'S FRIEND.

IT'S RICK JONES, HULK--REMEMBER? WE WERE *KIDNAPPED* AND BROUGHT DOWN HERE! YOU HAVE TO HELP US!

THERE'S A BAD MAN CALLED *TYRANNUS*. WE HAVE TO FIND HIM. *HE'S* THE ONE WHO WANTED TO HURT BETTY AND ME-- YOU, TOO.

HULK WILL FIND TYRANNUS-- THEN *SMASH* HIM!

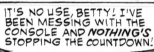

STRANGE... THE HULK JUST DEMOLISHED THE VERY DEVICE THAT BROUGHT HIM INTO EXISTENCE.

I WONDER IF SOMEWHERE IN THAT DIM BRAIN, HE KNOWS WHAT HE'S DONE.

FAAANTASTIC! THAT'S WHAT I CALL A DEMOLITION DERBY!

HULK FEELS... STRANGE.

MACHINE MEANT SOMETHING.

WAS SOMETHING.

GONE.

LISTEN -- THAT HEAVY CLANGING SOUND!

AND THE FLOOR'S SHAKING! YOU WIGGLING THOSE BIG TOES, HULK?

HULK NOT MOVING.

OH, BUT YOU WILL BE MOVING VERY SOON, CREATURE! OR YOU'LL BE STOMPED UNDERFOOT LIKE AN INSECT!

TYRANNUS!

YES! AND BECAUSE OF YOUR UNFORTUNATE DESTRUCTION OF MY GAMMA BOMB--THE TASK OF CONQUERING THE SURFACE WORLD HAS BEEN PUT BACK MONTHS-- YEARS!

BOOM

BUT WHAT IS TIME TO ONE WHO HAS LIVED CENTURIES, EH, DR. BANNER? I HAVE ALL ETERNITY TO SCHEME.

SHUT UP ABOUT PUNY BANNER!

HULK HATES BANNER!

I DON'T KNOW THE GENE- SIS OF YOUR HORRENDOUS TRANSFORMATION, DOCTOR--

--BUT THERE IS LITTLE YOUR BRUTISH ALTER-EGO CAN DO AGAINST THIS ROBOT CONSTRUCTED OF THE STRONGEST METALS KNOWN...

TWIIING

...AND POSSESSING COUNTLESS WEAPONS OF MY OWN DESIGN.

AARRGH! HULK NOT NEED WEAPONS, ROBOT MAN!

THUNK

HULK IS THE STRONGEST ONE THERE IS!

WHAT IS THE SOURCE OF THE MONSTER'S STRENGTH?! COULD I BRING SUCH A BEING UNDER MY CONTROL?

WHROOM

NOW HULK WILL SMASH ROBOT MAN WITH STUPID TALKING HEAD!

ROBOT MAN *GONE*-- COVERED BY ROCKS. HULK NOT MISS ROBOT MAN.

BUT HULK FEEL STRANGE-- WEAK. HULK FEEL LIKE... LIKE...

...*PUNY* BANNER AGAIN.

I'M MYSELF ONCE MORE.

RICK-- BETTY-- YOU'RE *OKAY!*

HEY, BRUCE, WAY TO GO! YOU SHOULD'VE SEEN THE HULK *TRASH* TYRANNUS AND HIS GOONS.

NO! THE FOUNTAIN-- IT'S BEEN *BURIED* UNDER *COUNTLESS* TONS OF ROCK!

WITHOUT IT I'LL *AGE*-- I'LL GROW OLD AND *DIE!*

HERE... A FEW *PRECIOUS* DROPS-- MUST *HAVE* THEM KEEP MY *YOUTH*-- MY *STRENGTH!*

TYRANNUS MUST *LIVE* TO CONQUER-- *CONQUER!* IT IS MY DESTINY! MERLIN WILL *NOT* DENY ME!

LET'S GO! I CAN'T HEAR ANY MORE OF THIS.

BRUCE, I HAVE A QUESTION. EARLIER, YOU GAVE TYRANNUS THE FORMULA HE NEEDED TO ACTIVATE THE GAMMA BOMB.

D-DID YOU *REALLY* GIVE HIM THE CORRECT EQUATION-- OR WERE YOU JUST BUYING TIME FOR US?

I DID WHAT I BELIEVED WAS *PRUDENT* AT THAT MOMENT, BETTY... WHAT I FELT-- WHAT I *KNEW* WAS DEMANDED OF ME IN THAT CIRCUMSTANCE.

MORE I CAN'T SAY!

WELL, YOU JUST SAID A *MOUTHFUL*, DOC. THAT WAS A DANDY SPEECH.

Y'KNOW, YOU MAY HAVE A BRIGHT FUTURE IN *POLITICS*. I CAN HEAR IT NOW...

...FRIENDS, ROMANS, COUNTRY-MEN-- LEND ME YOUR EARS! *HEY!* GIMME A BREAK! THE SCENERY GOT TO ME.

THE END.

Think of any Marvel character and chances are the first name that comes to mind is male, but you know what they say about the female of the species... The Marvel Universe boasts plenty of formidable females, too - both good and bad. Here's an introduction to just four of them.

THE SENSATIONAL SHE-HULK
Los Angeles lawyer Jennifer Walters is Bruce Banner's cousin. When she was shot by a gangster, Banner improvised a blood transfusion at the scene, but his irradiated blood turned her into a female version of the legendary Incredible Hulk. As well as starring in her own comics and animated TV series, she was also a member of The Avengers and a temporary stand-in for The Fantastic Four's Thing.

JEAN GREY
Along with her partner, Scott Summers, Jean Grey is the longest-serving member of the X-Men and Professor Xavier's star pupil. Originally known as Marvel Girl, she became known as The Phoenix in the relaunched X-Men of the mid-70's and had telekinetic abilities that enabled her to control people and objects through willpower alone. She finally married Scott in a 1994 issue of X-Men.

ELEKTRA
Elektra was originally Matt Murdock's university girlfriend, only to become Daredevil's deadly enemy. After the death of her father, she fled in her grief to the Far East to become a ninja, returning to work as an assassin for evil villain The Kingpin. Old feelings often resurfaced during fights between Elektra and Daredevil, and she died in his arms after a battle with fellow assassin Bullseye, only to be resurrected again a few years later.

THE BLACK WIDOW
The Black Widow began as a KGB agent whose weapon was a bite that gave her victims a stunning electric shock. After defecting to the United States, she worked for Marvel's intelligence agency, S.H.I.E.L.D., and has in recent years worked closely with Captain America to lead The Avengers. She has had romantic links with fellow Avenger Hawkeye, as well as with super hero Daredevil.

SUPER VILLAINS

The Marvel Universe is just crawling with evil villains - lucky there are so many super heroes to keep 'em under control! Listed below are just some of the lowlife that have appeared so far. See if you can find them all in the wordsquare: they read forwards, backwards, up, down and diagonally.

W	U	R	E	T	S	A	M	T	E	P	P	U	P
N	L	B	R	O	A	B	G	M	S	D	E	T	S
A	T	G	N	A	N	O	R	Y	U	M	E	R	U
M	R	K	L	D	D	M	E	S	T	A	S	E	P
E	O	C	Z	Q	M	I	E	T	C	G	P	H	O
L	N	N	I	F	A	N	N	E	A	N	Y	T	T
O	S	K	E	P	N	A	G	R	L	E	L	N	C
M	O	J	L	V	B	T	O	I	A	T	A	K	O
L	E	A	D	E	R	I	B	O	G	O	C	I	R
I	Y	T	W	V	N	O	L	G	L	P	O	N	O
Z	E	M	O	H	A	N	I	P	K	B	P	G	T
A	J	U	G	G	E	R	N	A	U	T	A	P	C
R	N	O	I	P	R	O	C	S	K	U	P	I	O
D	O	C	T	O	R	D	O	O	M	M	U	N	D

MAGNETO   SCORPION   MOLE MAN
JUGGERNAUT   MYSTERIO   LOKI
ABOMINATION   TOAD   DIABLO
APOCALYPSE   SANDMAN   ZEMO
LEADER   VENOM   PUPPET MASTER
LIZARD   GREEN GOBLIN   ULTRON
GALACTUS   DOCTOR DOOM
KINGPIN   DOCTOR OCTOPUS

58

Profile: THE FANTASTIC FOUR

When scientific genius Reed Richards took his prototype spaceship on a test flight with best friend Ben Grimm, girlfriend Susan Storm and her young brother, Johnny, he had not foreseen the dangers that awaited them in space. A shower of cosmic rays forced them to crash land back on earth, where they emerged from the ship's wreckage with superhuman powers.

Reed Richards became Mister Fantastic, Ben Grimm became The Thing, Susan Storm was now The Invisible Woman and Johnny Storm, The Human Torch. The Fantastic Four were born!

MISTER FANTASTIC

Real name: Reed Richards

Super hero qualities: Becomes highly elastic and can stretch his rubbery body into almost any shape.

THE INVISIBLE WOMAN

Real name: Susan Richards (nee Storm)

Super heroine qualities: Can make herself and any object invisible; is able to surround herself with invisible force fields.

THE HUMAN TORCH

Real name: Johnny Storm

Super hero qualities: Bursts into flames without any harm to himself and in this state can fly.

THE THING

Real name: Ben Grimm

Super hero qualities: His impenetrable, rock-like orange hide gives him superhuman strength.

THE MANHATTAN HEADQUARTERS OF THE FABULOUS *FANTASTIC FOUR*... A QUARTET OF INDIVIDUALS WHO RECEIVED UNIQUE POWERS WHEN COSMIC RAYS PENETRATED AN EXPERIMENTAL SPACESHIP THEY WERE PILOTING.

NOW, F.F. LEADER REED RICHARDS HAS CALLED HIS TEAM-MATES TOGETHER IN THE SPACE/TIME LAB OF FOUR FREEDOMS PLAZA...

SUSAN, BEN, JOHNNY-- I CALLED YOU IN HERE BECAUSE I'M ON THE VERGE OF VISUALLY PENETRATING A HERETOFORE UNKNOWN REGION.

IT'S SOMETHING YOU SHOULD *ALL* BE HERE TO SEE.

YEAH? WHATTAYA DOIN'-- SNEAKIN' A PEAK IN *MADONNA'S* BEDROOM WINDOW?

KLIK

I'M OPENING THE VISI-SCREEN PORTAL. YOU'LL SEE WHAT *NO* HUMAN EYES HAVE *EVER* SEEN-- IN SECONDS!

PTSSSS

WHOA! YOU SURE YOU KNOW WHAT YER GETTIN' INTO, MISTER?

OH, REED! IT'S *HORRIFYING!* I-I COULD NEVER HAVE IMAGINED ANYTHING LIKE THIS!

YEAH... DITTO.

THE TIES THAT BIND

RALPH MACCHIO
WRITER

ANDY KUHN
PENCILER

HARRY CANDELARIO
INKER

MIKE HIGGINS
LETTERER

KEVIN TINSLEY
COLORIST

MARK BERNARDO
EDITOR

BOB HARRAS
CHIEF

OF COURSE, PRELIMINARY EXPLORATION IS A NECESSITY. AND THAT'S WHY I WANT YOU, BEN, TO SUIT UP AND TAKE THE FIRST STEP INTO THIS VAST, NEW AREA.

DO *WHAT*?! IF YOU THINK I'M PUTTIN' EVEN ONE 'A MY LITTLE TOOTSIES IN THERE, PAL-- YER *NUTS*!

COME ON, THING, YA BIG SCAREDY CAT! IF *YOU* WON'T GO, THE *HUMAN TORCH* IS READY, WILLING AND ABLE!

THANK YOU FOR THE OFFER, SON. BUT, TRUTHFULLY, I NEED SOMEONE WITH A BIT MORE *MATURITY...*

...SOMEONE WITH MORE PATIENCE AND EXPERIENCE. YOU UNDERSTAND.

SURE! IF YOU THINK THAT ORANGE PILE OF ROCKS IS MORE MATURE, MORE CAPABLE-- *FINE!* THEN I'M SPLITTIN'.

OH, JOHNNY-- DON'T!

LISTEN, YOU KNOW REED CAN BE A LITTLE GRUFF WITHOUT REALIZING IT. I'M SURE HE DIDN'T MEAN ANY HARM.

I KNOW HE'S YOUR HUSBAND, SUE, BUT THAT'S *NO* EXCUSE FOR INSULTING ME THAT WAY!

IF HE DOESN'T SEE ME AS AN EQUAL MEMBER OF THIS TEAM--

64

--I'M *OUTTA* HERE!

SHOOM

THE *TRAPSTER, THUNDRA* AND MY *NEW* RECRUIT-- THE *SANDMAN.* EACH WITH UNIQUE ABILITIES TO RING DOWN THE FANTASTIC FOUR.

"THE *TRAPSTER*... A CRUDE FELON WHO DEVELOPED A *SUPER-ADHESIVE PASTE*...

"...AND AN EFFECTIVE GUN WITH WHICH TO DIRECT IT AT AN ADVERSARY. HIS SOLO ENCOUNTERS WITH THE HUMAN TORCH HAVE BEEN WELL-DOCUMENTED.

"*THUNDRA,* A HUGE, ENORMOUSLY POWERFUL WARRIOR WOMAN I ENCOUNTERED RECENTLY.

"SHE CLAIMED SHE WAS FROM THE FUTURE AND HAD COME BACK-- BECAUSE IT WAS HER *DESTINY* TO FIND AND DEFEAT THE STRONGEST MALE OF OUR ERA.

"WHETHER HER STORY IS TRUE IS QUESTIONABLE. BUT I BELIEVE SHE POSSESSES ENOUGH STRENGTH TO CONTEND WITH THE MIGHTY *THING.*

"INDEED, HER PERFORMANCE HERE TODAY LEADS ME TO BELIEVE SHE CAN *CRUSH* HIM IN UNARMED COMBAT.

" FINALLY, THERE IS THE *SANDMAN*, WHOM I RECENTLY BROKE OUT OF PRISON.

"HIS INCREDIBLE ABILITY TO ALTER THE MOLECULES OF HIS SANDY BODY INTO VARIOUS CONFIGURATIONS--

"--MAKES HIM A MOST FORMIDABLE ANTAGONIST AGAINST ANY OF RICHARDS' FOURSOME.

UGH! SAND PARTICLES CAUGHT IN MY EYES!

YOU CARELESS *FOOL!* I LOST CONCENTRATION BECAUSE OF YOUR INTERFERENCE IN MY DRILL!

THAT'S TOUGH *TOENAILS*, BABE! NEXT TIME WEAR GLASSES.

LET THERE BE NO DISPUTES.

WIZARD, I GROW WEARY OF THESE DELAYS. YOU PROMISED I WOULD CONFRONT THE STRONGEST MALE ON YOUR WORLD.

AND SO YOU SHALL. THE TIME FOR EXERCISES IS OVER.

ALL IS IN READINESS FOR OUR TAKEOVER OF THE SKYSCRAPER HEADQUARTERS OF OUR ENEMIES!

ONE OF THEIR NUMBER-- THE HUMAN TORCH--HAS SEPARATED FROM THE GROUP IN ANGER...LEAVING ONLY THREE TO DEAL WITH.

I AM GOING TO DRAW THE TRIO OUT OF THEIR PRECIOUS FOUR FREEDOMS PLAZA THAT WE MAY PROPERLY PREPARE IT FOR THEIR RETURN.

I HAVE BEEN ABLE TO OBSERVE REED RICHARDS AND HIS COHORTS FOR WEEKS, TAKING CAREFUL NOTE OF THEIR EVERY MOVE. IT HAS BEEN AN INVALUABLE ADDITION TO MY KNOWLEDGE.

AND KNOWLEDGE IS THE GREATEST OF POWERS.

IT WAS YOUR SAND POWER THAT ALLOWED INFILTRATION OF PRECIOUS HEADQUARTERS, ENABLING YOU TO PLACE THOSE MINIATURE CAMERAS THERE. WELL DONE.

THANKS, WIZ.

NOW TO DRAW THE F.F. OUT, I WILL RELEASE NUMEROUS EXPLOSIVE DEVICES THAT WILL ATTACH THEMSELVES TO THE SIDES OF THE SURROUNDING BUILDINGS.

MULTIPLE EXPLOSIONS OUTSIDE! WE'D BETTER GET OUT THERE! PEOPLE ARE IN DANGER! *LET'S GO!*

YA DON'T HAVETA TELL ME *TWICE,* MISTER! SURE WISH JOHNNY WAS STILL HERE.

THE LAD'LL BE BACK, I'M SURE. MEANWHILE I'M ACTIVATING OUR *SECURITY SYSTEMS* TO ENSURE NO INTRUDERS ENTER WHILE WE'RE OUT.

MOMENTS LATER, ON THE STREETS...

THOSE LARGE DISCS ON THE SIDES OF THE BUILDINGS... I SAW ONE EXPLODE AS WE RAN OUT. THEY'RE THE SOURCE OF THE EXPLOSIONS WE HEARD.

I WONDER WHY THEY'RE *BIG* ENOUGH FER EASY PICKIN'S. THE GUY THAT PUT 'EM UP THERE MUST BE A *REAL* AMATEUR.

DON'T TAKE THIS AT FACE VALUE, BEN. THESE DISCS COULD JUST BE THE TIP OF THE ICEBERG.

BUT WE *STILL* HAVE TO REMOVE THEM BEFORE THEY EXPLODE. AND *THIS* ONE'S...

...GOING RIGHT IN THE EAST RIVER!

WAH BOOM

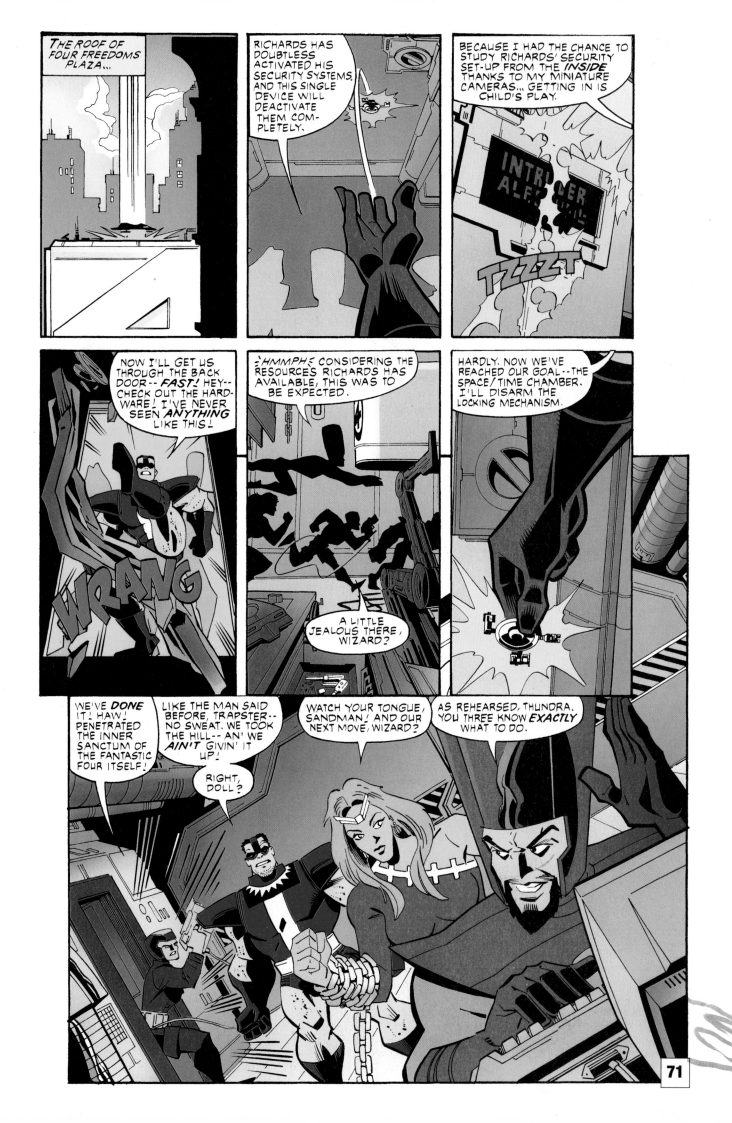

I DON'T GET IT, STRETCH. WE TAKE OUT ALL'A THESE EXPLOSIVE THINGIES AND THEN WAIT FER THE BAD GUY TA SHOW UP AN'--

--ZILCH, NADA, NOTHIN', WHAT'D WE MISS? ARE WE LOSIN' OUR TOUCH? AIN'T WE SHOWERIN' ENOUGH?

I DON'T BELIEVE SO, OLD FRIEND-- ONCE WE TAKE OUR PRIVATE ELEVATOR BACK UP TO OUR OWN FLOORS, WE'LL FIND OUT.

REED, YOU SOUND SO OMINOUS. WHAT AREN'T YOU SAYING?

AHH... DON'T MIND HIM, SUZIE. HE'S GOTTA WORRY ABOUT SOMETHIN'.

TIIING

HEY-- WHAT IN SAM HILL'S GOIN' ON? THE ELEVATOR DOOR OPENS-- AN I GOT MY BEAK STICKIN' IN *ANOTHER* ONE BEHIND IT?!

THAT'S NO DOOR, BEN. IT'S *PASTE*... HARDENED PASTE.

SOMEONE'S TRYIN' TO KEEP US FROM GOING UP.

YEAH?

WELL, IT AIN'T HAPPENIN'!

THWAM

BRACE YOUR- SELVES. OUR ENEMIES ARE ALREADY INSIDE.

SO THEY LURED US OUT WITH THEM STUPID FIREWORKS-- THEN MADE THEIR MOVE.

NICE. REAL NICE.

MOMENTS LATER IN THE SPACE/TIME CHAMBER...

AHH, HOW NICE OF YOU ALL TO DROP IN.

YOU WERE **NOT** THE CHALLENGE I HAVE KNOWN IN THE PAST, RICHARDS. UNBEKNOWNST TO YOU, THE SANDMAN INFILTRATED FOUR FREEDOMS PLAZA AND PLACED MICRO-CAMERAS--

--WHERE I COULD EASILY OBSERVE YOU. ONCE I SAW THE TORCH DESERT YOU EARLIER, I KNEW THE TIME WAS RIPE--

--TO CREATE THE DIVERSION NECESSARY TO GET YOU OUT OF YOUR HEADQUARTERS SO YOU COULD BE REPLACED.

NOW THAT YOU KNOW **WHY** YOU WERE DEFEATED, I'M OPENING THE LOCKS INTO SUB-SPACE, INTO WHICH YOU AND YOUR COMPANIONS WILL SOON BE THRUST-- TO **DIE!**

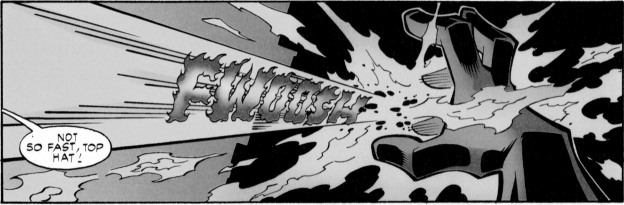

FWOOSH

NOT SO FAST, TOP HAT!

WHO--? THE **HUMAN TORCH**?! BUT YOU LEFT IN A HUFF BEFORE?! WHY ARE YOU HERE NOW?

74

SOME INVISIBLE PROJECTILES SHOULD KEEP YOU OFF-BALANCE.

MY TURN!

THIS REINFORCED FORCE FIELD IS SPREAD WALL TO WALL AND I'LL USE IT TO KEEP PUSHING YOU BACK-- BACK-- BACK!

SHE'S *GOT* ME! NOWHERE TO GO-- CAN'T SLIP PAST IT NO MATTER WHAT I DO!

AGAINST THE WALL-- *TRAPPED*-- JUST LIKE THE CELL I WAS TRAPPED IN BACK IN PRISON. NO WAY OUT!

NO WAY OUT!

WOW! REMIND ME TO STAY ON YOUR GOOD SIDE, SIS! THAT WAS *AWESOME!*

NOoOO...

I DON'T THINK IT WAS JUST *PHYSICAL* PRESSURE THAT STOPPED HIM, JOHNNY. HE SEEMED TO COLLAPSE *MENTALLY*.

78 ④

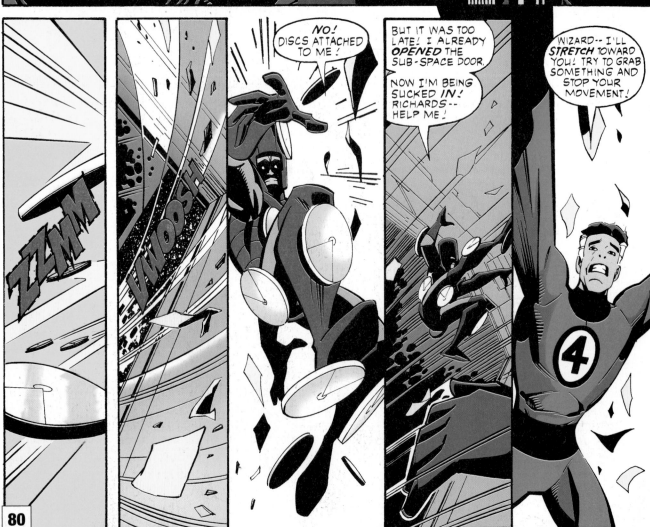

BACK IN F.F. HEADQUARTERS...

SO YOU CONCOCTED THIS SCHEME TO FLUSH THE WIZARD OUT AND LET ONLY *JOHNNY* IN ON IT SO OUR REACTIONS TO HIS SUDDEN DEPARTURE WOULD BE GENUINE.

AND IT WORKED LIKE A CHARM, SIS.

HEY, STRINGBEAN, DON'T FEEL *TOO BAD* ABOUT NOT RETRIEVIN' THE WIZARD FROM SUB-SPACE. IF ANYBODY COULD SURVIVE TO COME BACK AND *HARASS* US AGAIN--HE'S A GENT.

YA DID YER BEST!

I APPRECIATE THE SENTIMENT, BEN, BUT TO LOSE ANY HUMAN LIFE--EVEN ONE AS MISGUIDED AS THE WIZARD'S-- IS A TRAGEDY.

I'M GOING BACK IN THERE AND REDOUBLE MY EFFORTS TO FIND HIM.

Y'KNOW, I'M WONDERIN' WHAT HAPPENED TO THEM OTHER THREE CLOWNS. GUESS THEY DECIDED TA SKEDADDLE WHILE THEY COULD.

BLOCKS AWAY...

WHAT A BUNCH O' *LOSERS!* I SHOULD'A STAYED IN THE CLINK! IT WOULD'A BEEN LESS EMBARRASSIN'!

AWW, GO FIND AN EMPTY HOURGLASS AND GET A JOB, SANDBAG!

QUIET! YOUR BICKERING IS DRIVING ME TO DISTRACTION!

MEN-- WHAT ELSE SHOULD I HAVE EXPECTED FROM THE INFERIOR SEX? GRRRR...

RUFF

82

THE EVER-LOVIN' END!

Are you as well up on the Marvel Universe as you think you are? Test yourself with these ten questions and give yourself 10 points for each correct answer. Anything less than 60% and you've got homework to do!

1 Which Marvel super hero trained as a US Marine?
a) Spider-Man
b) Daredevil
c) The Punisher

2 In which year did The Fantastic Four make their debut?
a) 1951
b) 1961
c) 1971

3 The Sub-Mariner was Marvel's first mutant super hero. What was the colour of his skin under water?
a) Green
b) Orange
c) Pink

4 Which of the following is The Incredible Hulk's huge-skulled nemesis?
a) The Leader
b) Dr Doom
c) Galactus

5 Which member of The Fantastic Four was an astronaut?
a) Ben Grimm
b) Susan Storm
c) Reed Richards

6 Which Marvel super hero is blind?
a) Iron Man
b) Daredevil
c) The Human Torch

7 Which of the following was not a founder member of The Avengers?
a) Wolverine
b) The Wasp
c) Thor

8 Who is Marvel's super soldier?
a) Captain Marvel
b) Captain Britain
c) Captain America

9 Which member of the X-Men is a mutant Russian farm boy?
a) Nightcrawler
b) Colossus
c) Gambit

10 Who did disabled physicist Don Blake first become whilst trapped in a cave?
a) The Punisher
b) Thor
c) The Beast

Answers: 1.c) 2.b) 3.c) 4.a) 5.a) 6.b) 7.a) 8.c) 9.b) 10.b)

LOVE IS IN THE AIR

There's always time for romance, even in the busiest super hero's life! See if you can match each of the men below to their love interest.

Peter Parker	Mary Jane Watson
Betty Ross	Reed Richards
Bruce Banner	Elektra Natchios
Pepper Potts	Tony Stark
Matt Murdock	Susan Storm

X-Men X-Word

Writing towards the centre of the X-grid, fill in the names of the four X-Men in the squares below. Then rearrange the shaded letters to spell the name of their main adversary.

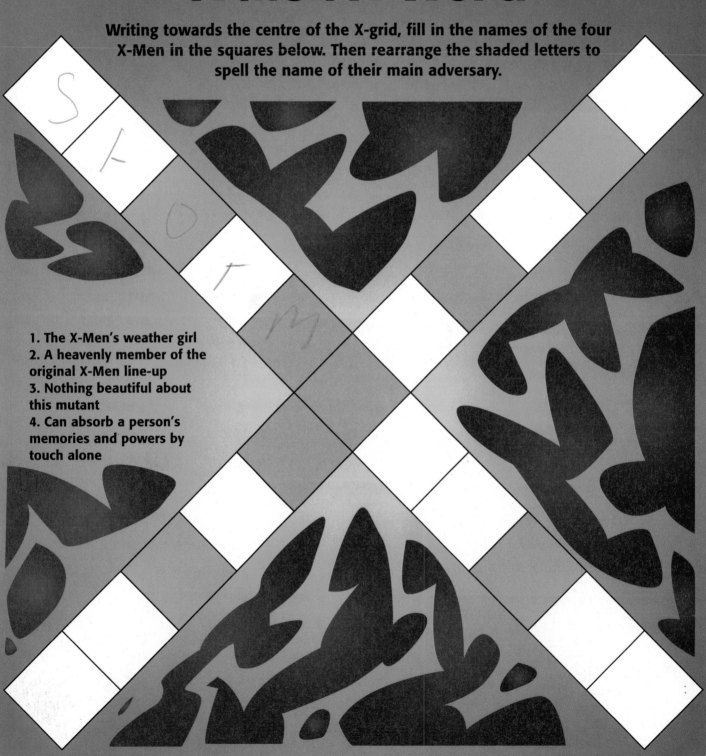

1. The X-Men's weather girl
2. A heavenly member of the original X-Men line-up
3. Nothing beautiful about this mutant
4. Can absorb a person's memories and powers by touch alone

Profile: The X-Men

The X-Men are a group of mutant youngsters with extraordinary abilities. Trained by Professor Charles Xavier at his School for Gifted Youngsters, they have been taught how to use their special powers for the betterment of mankind. They are sworn to defend a world that often fears and hates them.

WOLVERINE

Real name: Logan
Super hero qualities: Possesses animal-keen senses and indestructible Adamantium claws; can rapidly recover from any injury.

CYCLOPS

Real name: Scott 'Slim' Summers
Super hero qualities: Can fire a destructive power beam from his eyes.

STORM

Real name: Ororo Munroe
Super heroine qualities: Has the power to control the weather; can fly at subsonic speed.

GAMBIT

Real name: Remy LeBeau
Super hero qualities: Can charge any object with explosive kinetic energy; has unbreakable metal legs.

THE BEAST

Real name: Hank McCoy
Super hero qualities: Enormous hands and feet, superhuman agility and strength.

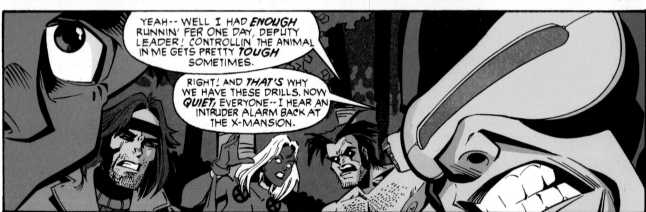

RUSHING TO THE MANSION'S SECOND FLOOR, THE GROUP OF YOUNG MUTANTS BURSTS INTO THE BEDROOM OF THE INSTITUTE'S LEADER, THE WHEELCHAIR-BOUND PROFESSOR **CHARLES XAVIER**-- THE FOREMOST TELEPATH ON THE PLANET.

QUICKLY! WE HAVE XAVIER **SEDATED** SO HE CANNOT RESPOND WITH A MENTAL ATTACK!

TAKE HIM FROM THE ROOM WHILE WE DEAL WITH THE STUDENTS.

WE HAD BEEN TOLD TO EXPECT THEM, AND IT SEEMS OUR APPEARANCE HAS SHOCKED THEM ENOUGH--

--FOR US TO EFFECT AN ESCAPE!

OUR QUARRY IS SECURE. NOW WE RETURN TO WUNDAGORE MOUNTAIN.

THEY'VE TAKEN THE PROFESSOR ONBOARD SOME AIRSHIP AND LIFTED OFF!

X-MEN-- LET'S REGROUP IN THE WAR ROOM AND PLOT STRATEGY.

BTWASH

I RIFLED HIS COMPUTER RECORDS AND LEARNED OF *YOU*, CHARLES XAVIER-- THE WORLD'S FOREMOST MUTANT *TELEPATH*. I KNEW THEN THAT I HAD TO BRING YOU HERE FOR MY PURPOSES.

THIS MACHINE WILL EXTEND YOUR MENTAL INFLUENCE TO *RUSSIA* WHERE YOU WILL FORCIBLY *CONTROL* THE MINDS OF RUSSIAN MISSILE TECHNICIANS AND *ORDER* THEM TO FIRE THEIR MISSILES AT THE UNITED STATES.

WHEN THE WEST RESPONDS, THE RESULTING ATOMIC WAR WILL *DESTROY* BOTH SIDES! BUT HERE, THE EVOLUTIONARY'S MASSIVE SAFEGUARDS WILL ALLOW US TO *SURVIVE*.

WE WILL NOT MEEKLY CRAWL FROM THE RUBBLE. THE MAN-BEAST AND HIS NEW MEN WILL RISE *PROUDLY* FROM THE ASHES OF CIVILIZATION AND CREATE A *NEW* ORDER OF THE WORLD!

WE WILL LAY CLAIM TO THE EARTH AND RULE FOR MILLENNIA! THIS I *SWEAR* AS THE SUPREME LIFEFORM OF THE WORLD!

AND YOU, MY DEAR PROFESSOR XAVIER, WILL MAKE THIS *ALL* POSSIBLE-- HOWEVER UNWILLING YOU ARE NOW. YOU WILL HAVE NO CHOICE.

YOU KEEP REFERRING TO THESE "NEW MEN." WHAT ARE THEY?

PLEASE...YOU AT LEAST OWE ME AN EXPLANATION.

NEW MEN-- REMOVE YOUR HELMETS. SHOW OUR GUEST THE TRUE FACES OF HIS CAPTORS.

INCREDIBLE-- ALL OF YOU ARE--

ANIMALS. YES... PRODUCTS OF THE EXPERIMENTS OF THE DEPARTED HIGH EVOLUTIONARY.

EACH OF US WAS ONCE A COMMON MAMMAL OR REPTILE OR AMPHIBIAN UNTIL WE WERE SUBJECTED TO THE GREAT EVOLUTIONARY RAY WHICH EVOLVED US COUNTLESS CENTURIES IN MERE MOMENTS.

AS KNIGHTS OF WUNDAGORE WE SERVED AT THE PLEASURE OF THE HIGH EVOLUTIONARY, UNTIL I-- AN EVOLVED WOLF-- RALLIED THE NEW MEN TO MY CAUSE. NOW THEY ARE MY SOLDIERS IN OUR WAR WITH HUMANITY!

NOW YOU'VE HEARD THE TALE, XAVIER. SO NOW I WILL HAVE YOU INJECTED WITH A HEAVY SEDATIVE--

--MAKING YOUR MAGNIFICENT MIND PLIABLE-- OPEN TO THE MAN-BEAST'S COMMANDS!

95

WITH THE PRESS OF A BUTTON, I WILL ACTIVATE THE MACHINERY THAT WILL CONTROL YOUR MIND...

...AND HARNESS YOUR IMMENSE ENERGIES IN MY SERVICE.

"YOU STRUGGLE, BUT THE SEDATIVE IS TOO POWERFUL. YOUR WILL IS MINE, CHARLES XAVIER!"

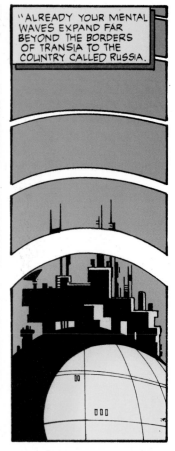

"ALREADY YOUR MENTAL WAVES EXPAND FAR BEYOND THE BORDERS OF TRANSIA TO THE COUNTRY CALLED RUSSIA."

"AND WITHIN THAT COUNTRY YOUR MENTAL ENERGIES SEEK OUT A CERTAIN MISSILE INSTALLATION."

"AND WITHIN THAT INSTALLATION YOUR BRAIN SEIZES THE MINDS OF THE PERSONNEL THERE."

"YOU COMMAND THEM TO TURN THEIR MISSILES ONCE MORE UPON WESTERN CITIES--AND READY THEM FOR IGNITION."

"SO DOES ARMAGEDDON BEGIN... THANKS TO YOU, AND YOUR MATCHLESS MUTANT MIND!"

LONDON
PARIS
NEW YORK
MADRID

96

WRANKK

RRRRRR-- *EXCELLENT!* XAVIER'S MIND DOMINANCE IS COMPLETE!

MY LIEGE-- THERE HAS BEEN A SECURITY *BREACH!* INTRUDERS HAVE BROKEN INTO WUNDAGORE PROPER.

CALL IN REINFORCEMENTS! *STOP THEM!*

YOU ARE *SURROUNDED,* INTRUDERS! *SURRENDER* AND YOU WILL NOT BE SLAIN!

GET A LOOK AT THE *KISSERS* ON THESE CLOWNS! LOOKS LIKE *RALPH LAUREN* GOT LOST IN THE *CENTRAL PARK ZOO* AND HANDED OUT *DESIGNER CLOTHES* TO THE RESIDENTS!

GET READY! I'M GOING FOR A WIDE ANGLE DISPERSAL PATTERN!

ON MY MARK...

...*NOW!*

TZEKKK

"EVEN NOW, THE KEYS ARE BEING TURNED, BEGINNING THE IGNITION SEQUENCE.

"IN MOMENTS, THE MISSILES, CARRYING THEIR DEADLY PAYLOADS, WILL BE LAUNCHED!"

IF HE'S TELLING THE TRUTH, OUR ONLY CHANCE IS TO FREE THE PROFESSOR FROM THE MACHINERY--*FAST!* GO FOR IT, HANK!

AFFIRMATIVE, BUT METHINKS MR. FUR 'N' FANGS WILL HAVE TO BE DOWNED FIRST.

RIGHT, X-MEN...

AWRIGHT, BEASTIE BOY--BACK TO THE DOGHOUSE!

THAMM

MAYBE NEXT TIME!

LET'S SEE HOW YOU WITHSTAND A *CONCENTRATED* OPTIC BLAST!

EASILY--BECAUSE I HAVE SET UP A MENTAL *REPULSION SHIELD* WHICH NOTHING CAN PENETRATE!

NOTHIN! 'CEPT DESE KINETICALLY-CHARGED PLAYIN' CARDS!

ZZZMMM

NOT IF I REDUCE THEIR CHARGE TO *ZERO* WITH MY UNRIVALED MIND.

ZZZMMM

105

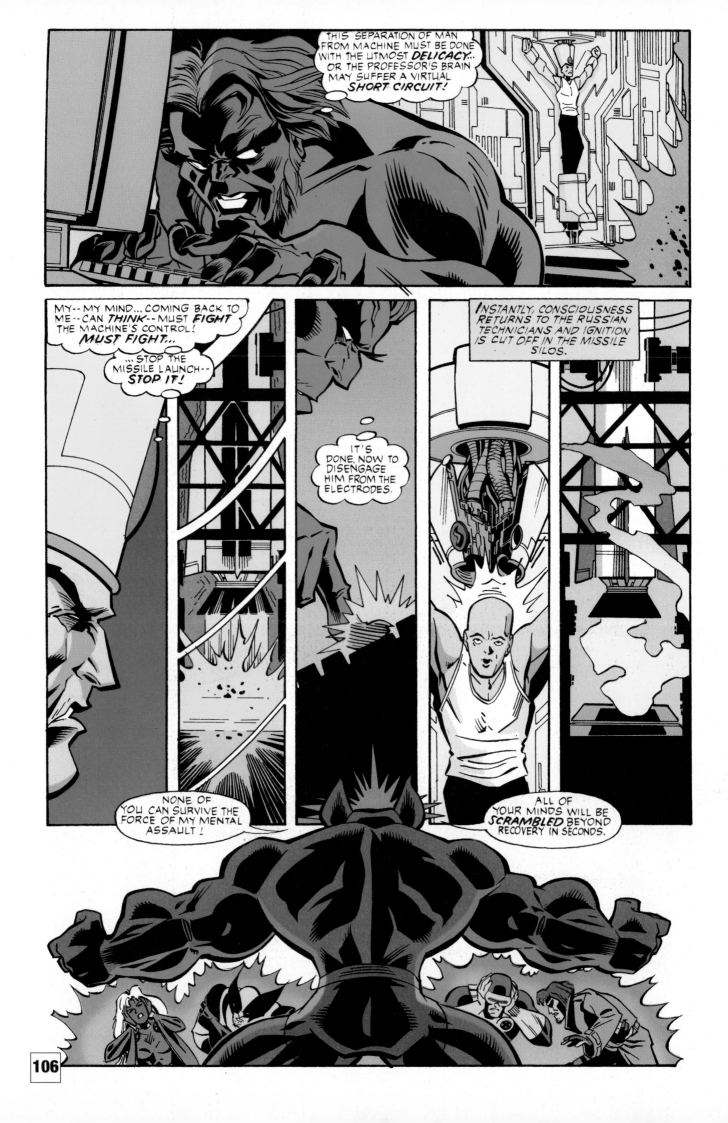

WAY BACK WHEN

Here come ten things you didn't know about the early days of your favourite Marvel characters...probably.

1 The first of many villains to do battle with Spider-Man was master of disguise The Chameleon, who appeared in the very first issue of Amazing Spider-Man back in 1962.

2 The 1960's marriage between Fantastic Four members Reed Richards and Susan Storm was the Marvel Universe's wedding of the century. It appeared in Fantastic Four Annual # 3 and was attended by all the Marvel main players, as well as The Beatles and other celebs of that era.

3 The Incredible Hulk hasn't always been that attractive shade of green. In his first appearance, his skin was grey, but had become its familiar green colour by issue 2.

4 Captain America originally had a young partner, Bucky Barnes. Top Marvel writer and editor Stan Lee had an aversion to kid sidekicks and killed him off in a story set at the end of World War 2 involving a booby-trapped Nazi plane.

5 Wolverine, star of The X-Men in the 1990's, was originally created for a 1970's issue of The Incredible Hulk.

6 Marvel's first space hero appeared in 1950 and lasted all of two issues. Marvel Boy, who was taken to live on Uranus as a child, returned to earth as a teen costumed crime-fighter.

7 There is only one thing capable of destroying the seemingly invincible Galactus: a tiny weapon called the Ultimate Nullifier, discovered by the Human Torch in a 1966 issue of The Fantastic Four.

8 The Incredible Hulk was one of the founding members of The Avengers, but quit in the next issue to become one of their adversaries.

9 Johnny Storm is not the original Human Torch. The first Marvel character of this name appeared in 1939 and was a robot that burst into flames on contact with oxygen, setting light to everything he touched.

10 One of the least known founding members of The Avengers was Henry Pym, the Ant-Man, a scientist who could reduce himself to the size of an insect and communicate with ants.